Snakehead

Super Sleep

Star Pilot

Super Bug

Super Gloo

Princess Mighty

Super Lady   Jaws

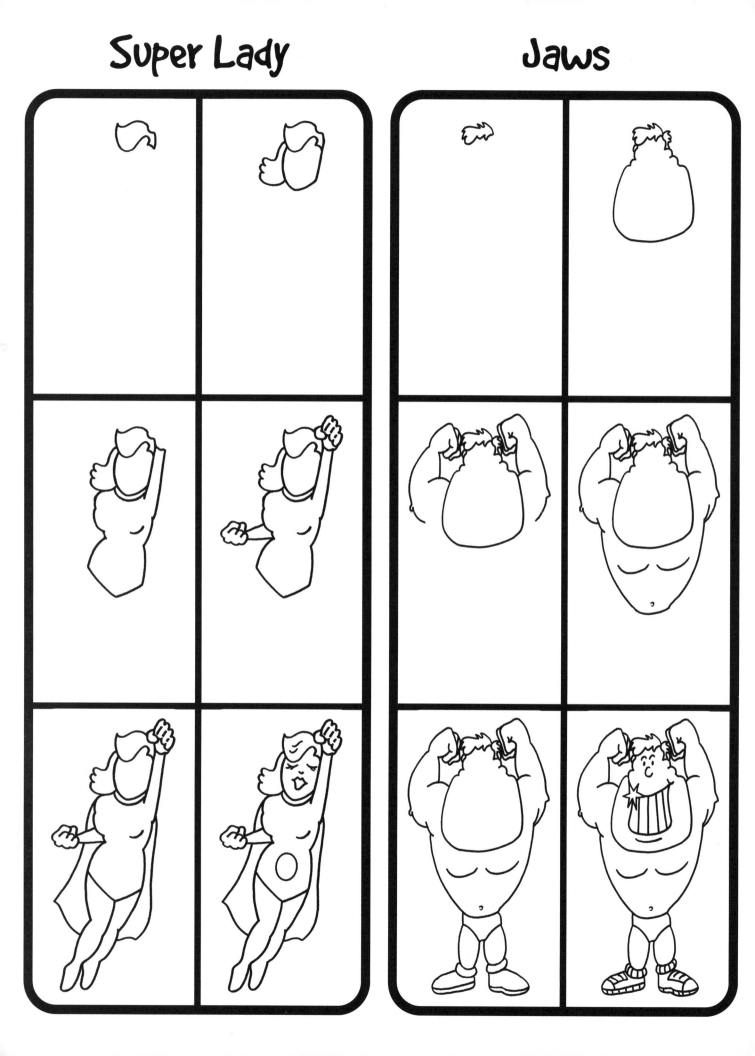

Super Thor

Super caveman

Super Duck   Hammer Head

Robot Warrior

Frogman

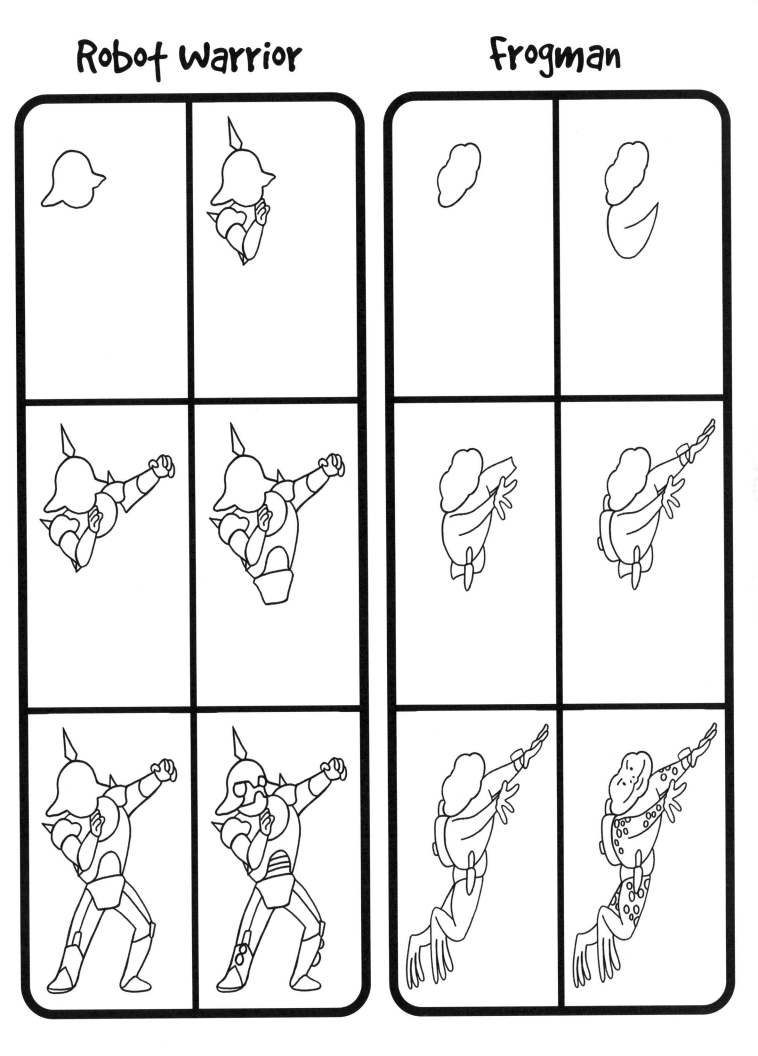

Karate King

Sky Diver

Super Star

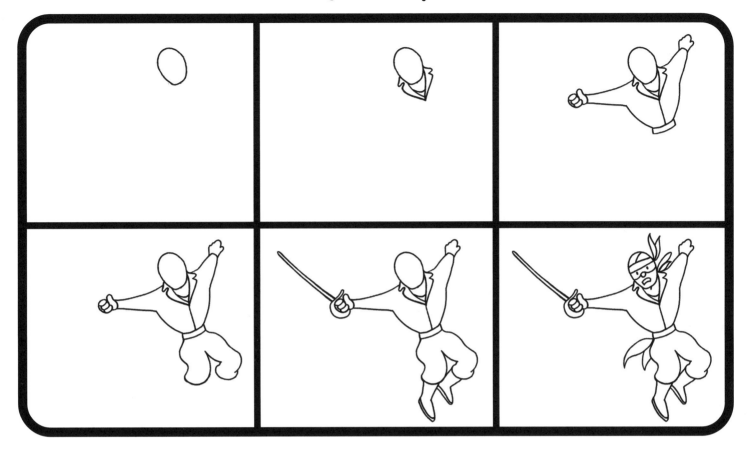

Sky Leaper

Lizardus

Surf Boarder

Space Queen

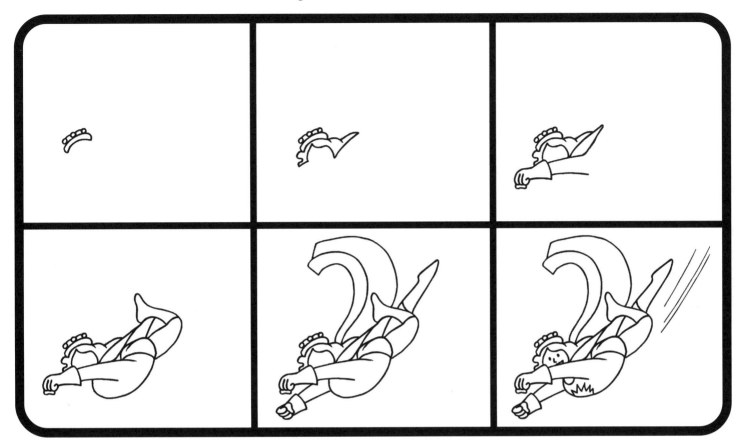

Super Charger

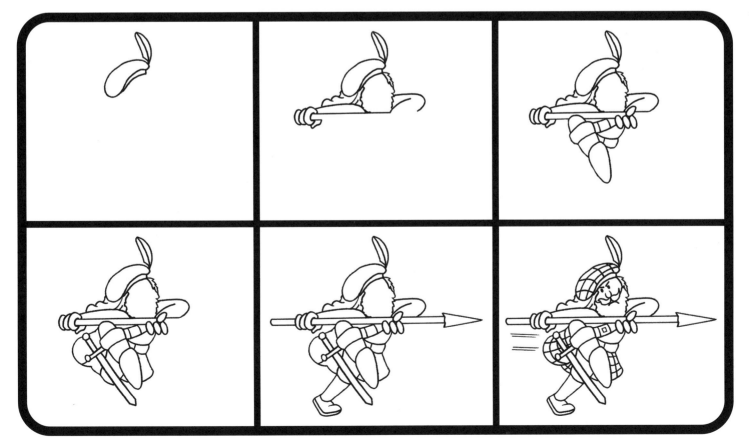

G.I.

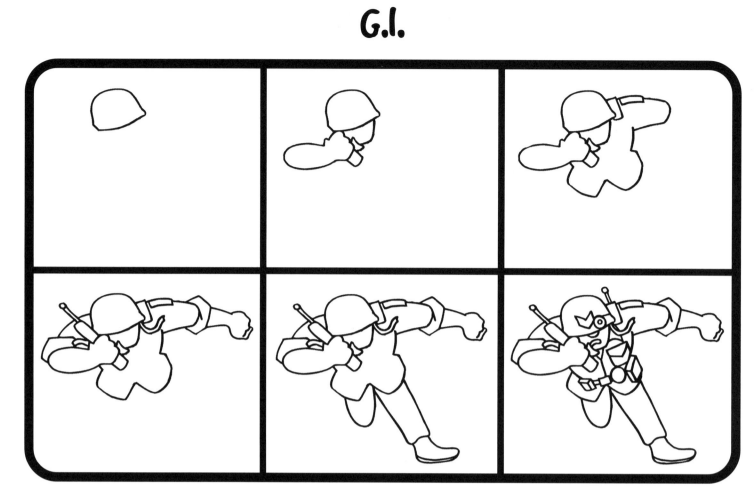

Markovian Lancer

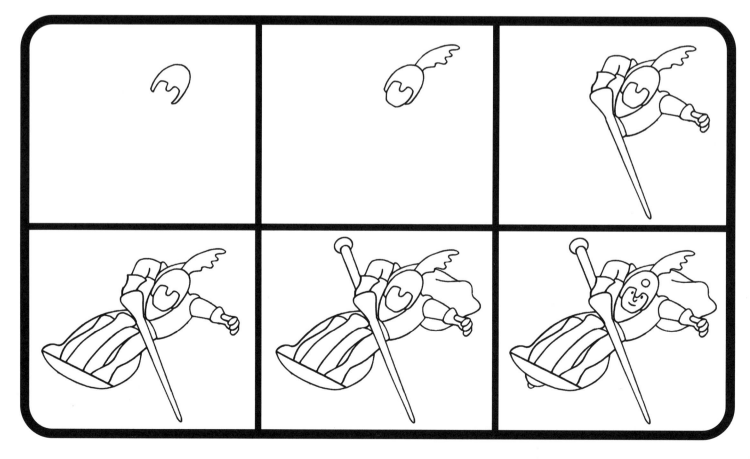

Greek Hero

Sky Scraper

Robo

Kango Kicker

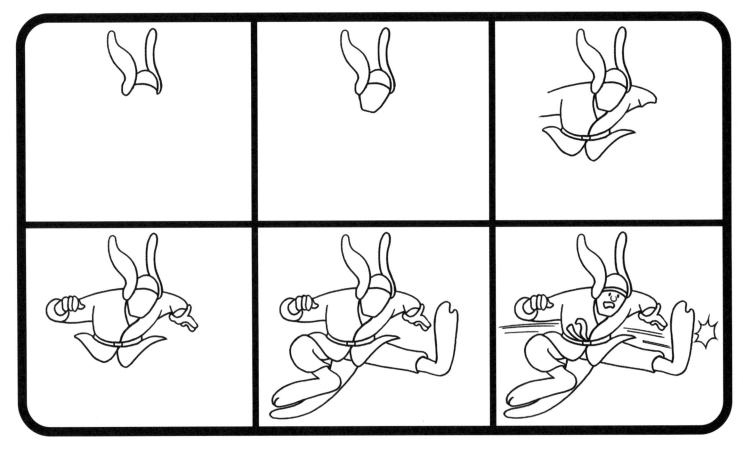

Star Chaser

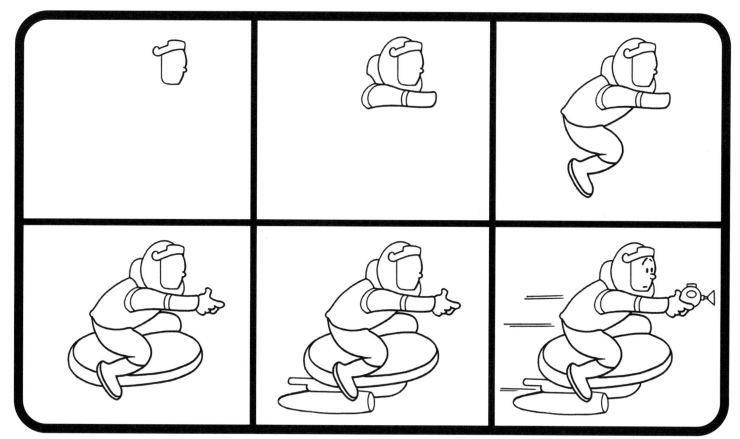

Rocky Hunter

Super Power

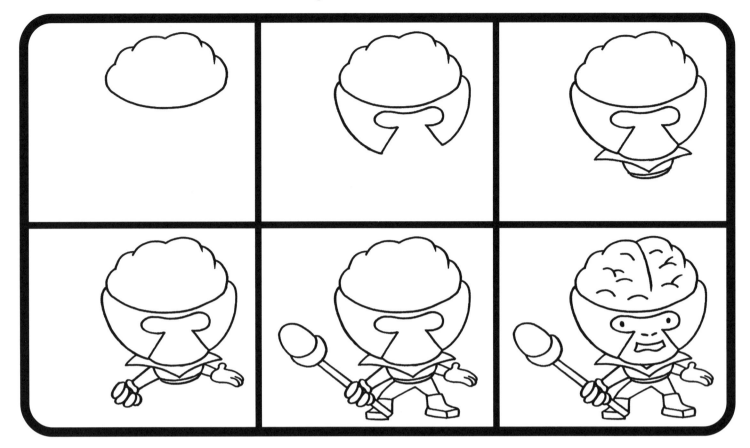

Android

Super Silly-us

Kongo

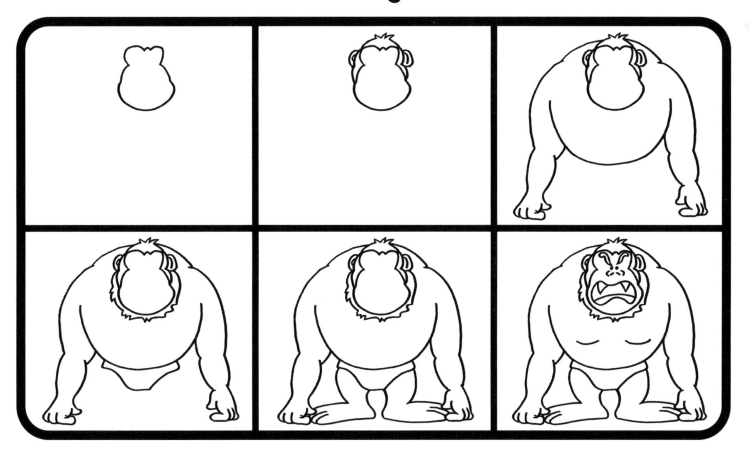

Star Skater

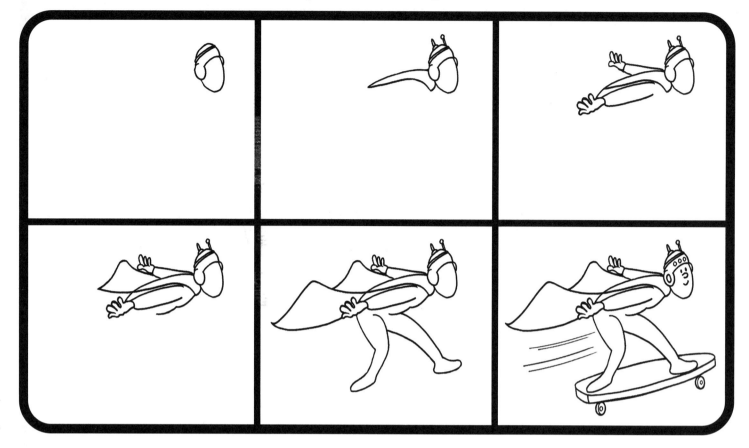

Arachnia

Layzar

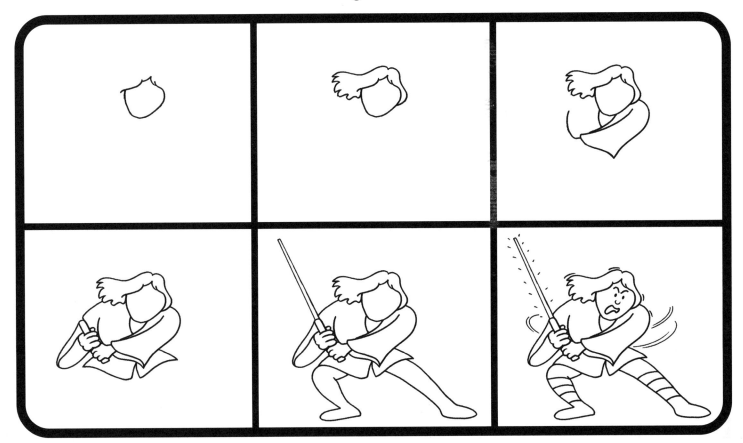

Super Swooper

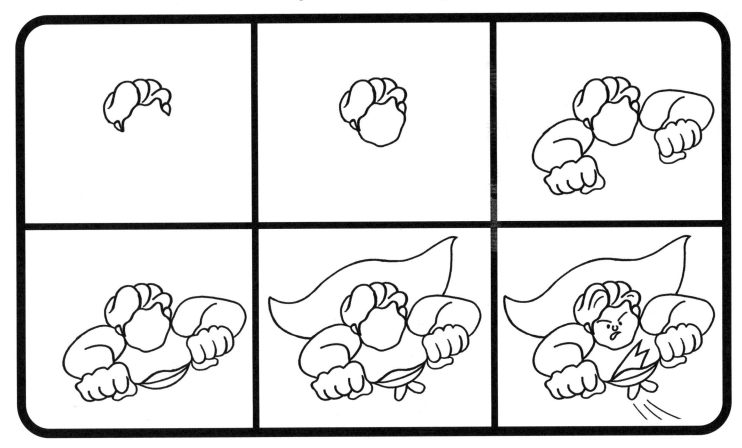

Super Nan

Barbarus

Super Flyer

Space Lancer

Super Spy

Goliath

Sitting Bull

Super Strongman

Space Saver

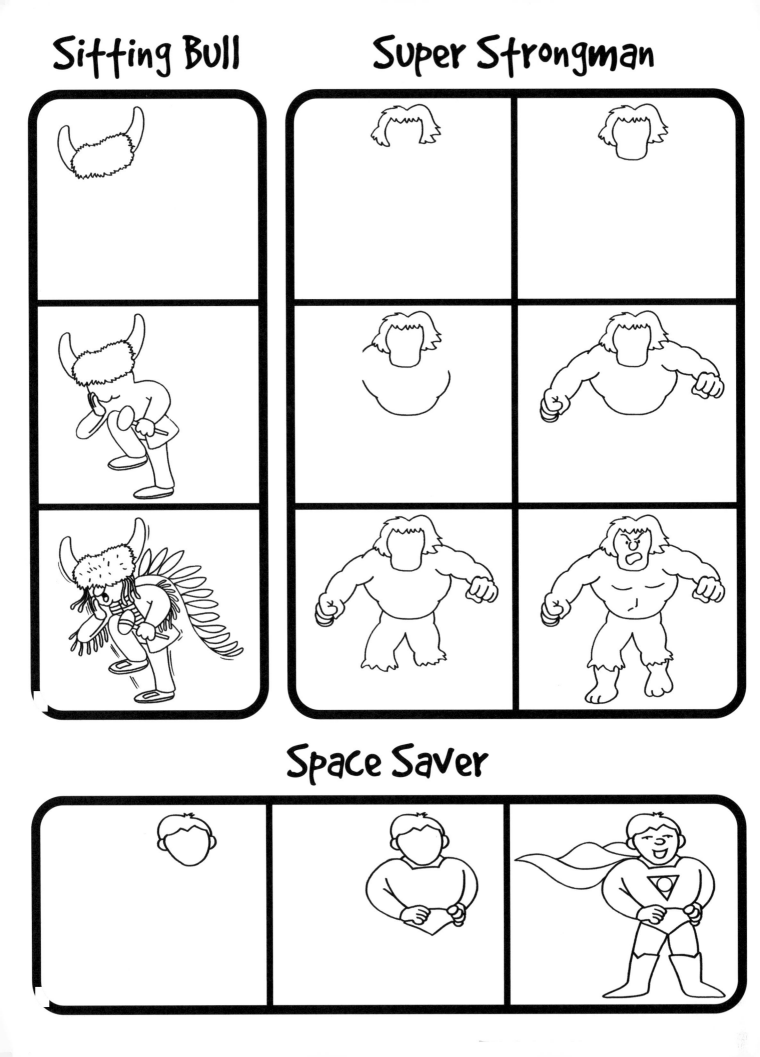

Iron Man

Super Boy

Super Woof

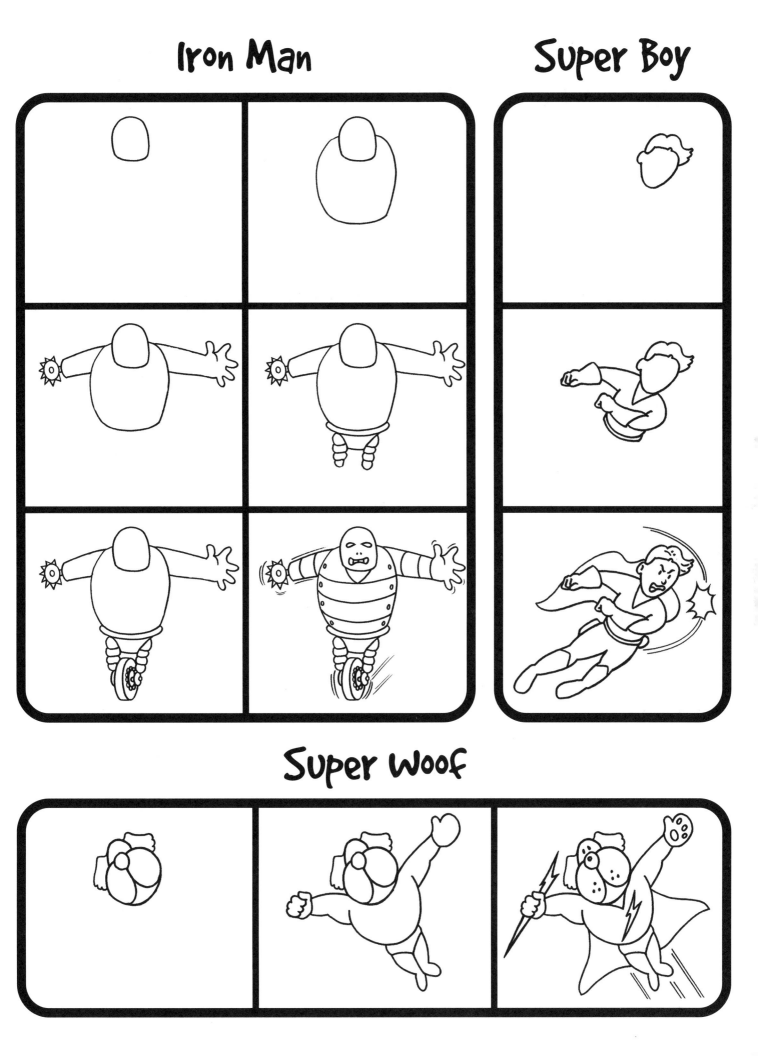

Super Bunny

Big Beard

Mighty Mog